The Jumping Contest

Published in the UK by Scholastic Education, 2022
Scholastic Distribution Centre, Bosworth Avenue, Tournament Fields, Warwick, CV34 6UQ
Scholastic Ireland, 89E Lagan Road, Dublin Industrial Estate, Glasnevin, Dublin, D11 HP5F

Printed by Ashford Colour Press
The book is made of materials from well-managed, FSC-certified forests
and other controlled sources.

A CIP catalogue record for this book is available from the British Library.

ISBN 978-0702-30905-2

Author
Catherine Baker
Editorial team
Rachel Morgan, Vicki Yates, Abbie Rushton, Liz Evans
Design team
Dipa Mistry, Justin Hoffmann, Andrea Lewis, We Are Grace
Illustrations
Csilla Köszeghy/Astound

Help your child to read!

This book practises words with more than one consonant next to each other, plus short vowel sounds (like 'be**st**' or '**st**uck'). Read these words with your child:

jumping   cricket   frog   spring

Your child may need help to read these common tricky words:

the   of   I   said   no   he   be   have   go

she   to

Before reading
- Look at the cover picture and read the title together. Read the back cover blurb to your child.
- Ask your child: *Can you point to the cricket, the frog and the rabbit on the cover? A cricket is like a grasshopper. Which one do you think would be best at jumping?*

During reading
- If your child gets stuck on a word, remind them to sound it out and then blend the sounds to read the word: s-p-r-i-ng, spring.
- If they are still stuck, show them how to read the word.
- Enjoy looking at the pictures together. Pause to talk about the story.

After reading
- Ask your child: *Were you surprised that the rabbit won the contest? Why?*
- *Do you think this story has a message? What might it be?* (For example: 'Don't be boastful; Try your best.')

Can you spot the chameleon on 6 pages?

The queen of the forest held a jumping contest.

Jumping Contest

4

"I will win!" said the cricket.
"I can spring up high!"

"No, I will win," said the frog.

"I can jump the highest!" he added.

"I might not be the best," said the rabbit.

The cricket sprang too high!
She got stuck.

She did not win.

The frog jumped... and flopped!
He landed next to the queen.

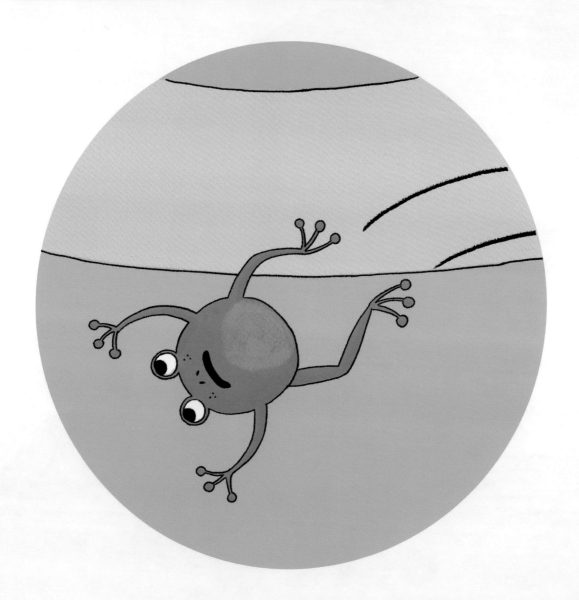

He did not win.

The rabbit did her best jump.
The queen got a shock!

14

"The rabbit is the best!" said the queen.

Retell the story

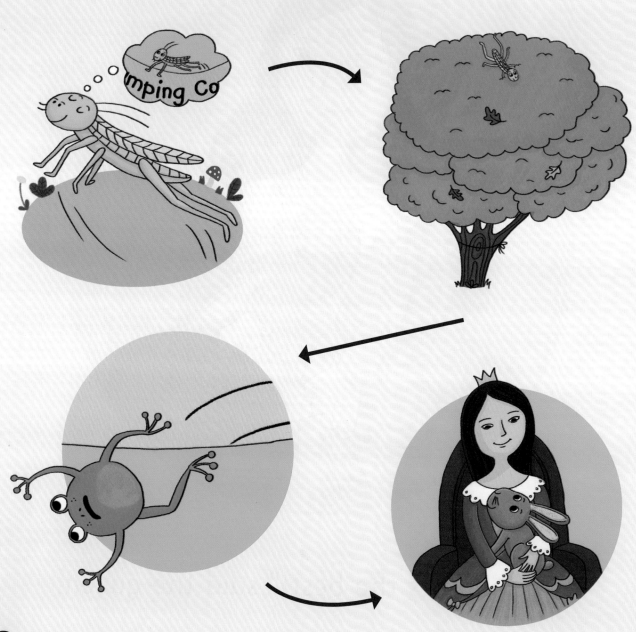